Stories of Santa

Up on the Housetop
Jolly Old St. Nicholas

A STORYBOOK OF TWO BELOVED SANTA SONGS

Hallmark

to

Corinne

from

Santa

Up on the Housetop

BENJAMIN R. HANBY

1. Up on the house - top____ rein - deer pause, Out jumps good old____ San - ta Claus;
2. First comes the stock - ing of lit - tle Nell, Oh, dear San - ta____ fill it well;
3. Next comes the stock - ing of lit - tle Will, Oh, just see what a glo - rious fill;

Down through the chim - ney with lots of toys, All for the lit - tle ones' Christ - mas joys!
Give her a dol - ly that laughs and cries, One that will o - pen and shut her eyes!
Here is a ham - mer and lots of tacks, Al - so a ball____ and whip that cracks.

Ho! Ho! Ho! Who would - n't go? Ho! Ho! Ho! Who would - n't go?___ Up on the house - top;
Ho! Ho! Ho! Who would - n't go? Ho! Ho! Ho! Who would - n't go?___ Up on the house - top;
Ho! Ho! Ho! Who would - n't go? Ho! Ho! Ho! Who would - n't go?___ Up on the house - top;

Click! Click! Click! Down through the chim - ney with good Saint Nick!
Click! Click! Click! Down through the chim - ney with good Saint Nick!
Click! Click! Click! Down through the chim - ney with good Saint Nick!

UP ON THE HOUSETOP

Up on the housetop reindeer pause,
Out jumps good old Santa Claus,
Down through the chimney with lots of toys,
All for the little ones' Christmas joys!

First comes the stocking of little Nell,
Oh, dear Santa, fill it well...

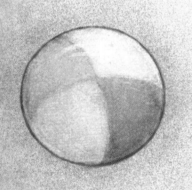

Give her a dolly that laughs and cries,
One that will open and shut her eyes!

Next comes the stocking of little Will,
Oh, just see what a glorious fill...

Here is a hammer and lots of tacks,
Also a ball...and a whip that cracks.

Ho! Ho! Ho!
Who wouldn't go?
Ho! Ho! Ho!
Who wouldn't go?

Up on the housetop…
Click! Click! Click!
Down through the chimney
with good Saint Nick.

Favorite gifts from Santa

Computer...
Bike...
Corinne doll...
Art kit...
Doll house...

Christmas songs and stories we love

Rudolph the red nose Raindeer.
...Jolly old saint nick...Up on
the housetop...

The best part of Christmas

I'm 8 because my birthday is on christmas eve. The presents. Suprises in our stockings. I get new ordaments every christmas.

SANTA AND ME

FAMILY PHOTOS

All I want for Christmas

_____
_____
_____
_____
_____
_____
_____
_____
_____
_____
_____
_____
_____
_____

Our best Christmas memories

_____
_____
_____
_____
_____
_____
_____
_____
_____
_____
_____
_____
_____
_____

Jolly Old Saint Nicholas

JOLLY OLD SAINT NICHOLAS

Jolly old Saint Nicholas,
Lean your ear this way!
Don't you tell a single soul
What I'm going to say.

Christmas Eve is coming soon.
Now, my dear old man,
Whisper what you'll bring to me,
Tell me, if you can.

When the clock is striking twelve,
When I'm fast asleep,
Down the chimney, broad and black,
With your pack you'll creep.

All the stockings you will find
Hanging in a row.
Mine will be the shortest one,
You'll be sure to know.

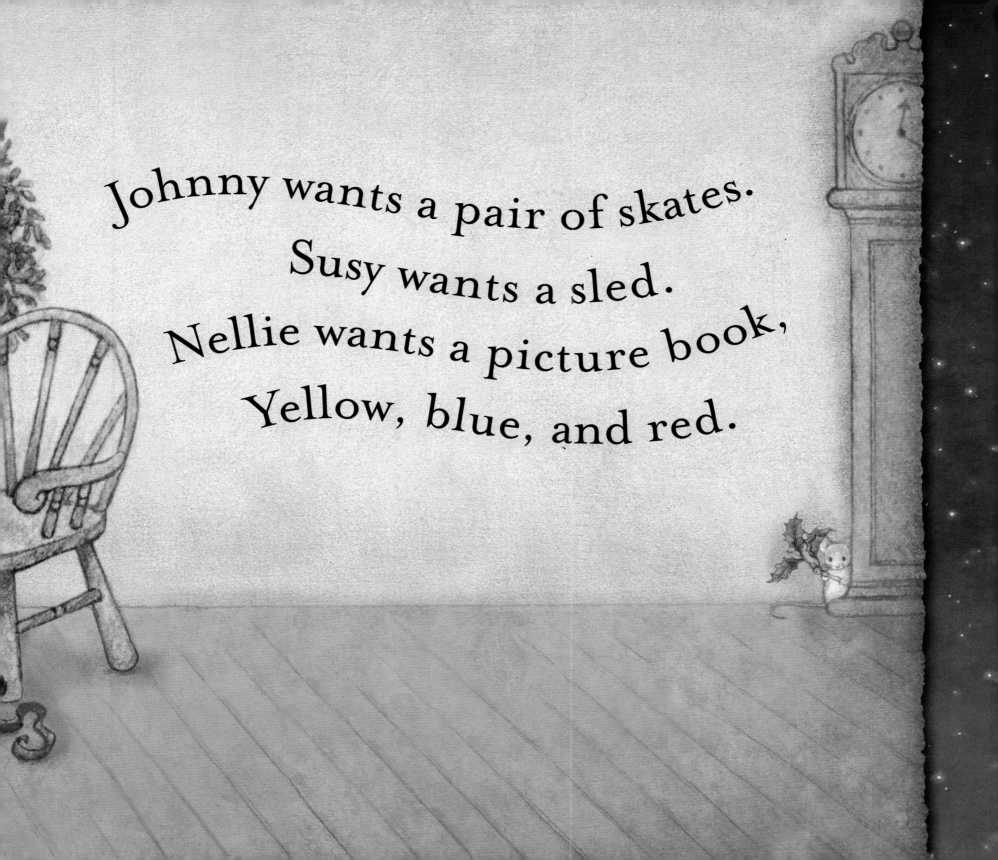

Johnny wants a pair of skates.
Susy wants a sled.
Nellie wants a picture book,
Yellow, blue, and red.

Now I think I'll leave to you
What to give the rest.
Choose for me, dear Santa Claus,
You will know the best.

Benjamin Russell Hanby

JULY 22, 1833 — MARCH 16, 1867

BENJAMIN HANBY was many things in his short lifetime —
a student, an abolitionist, a father, and a teacher.
But he is most remembered as a composer. And even though
he wrote more than 70 songs and hymns, including the Civil
War song *Darling Nelly Gray*, the one he's most known for is
Up on the Housetop. Some believe it was the first American song of
any importance about Santa Claus, and it is one of the first
secular Christmas songs composed in the United States. The
exact date of its writing isn't known, but it is thought to have
been created in the 1860s. While there isn't evidence to prove
it, some historians believe that Hanby also might have
composed *Jolly Old Saint Nicholas*, which dates back to about the
same time period and has similar musical styling and lyrics.